the Far Side

Also by Gary Larson

BEYOND THE FAR SIDE
BRIDE OF THE FAR SIDE
VALLEY OF THE FAR SIDE
IT CAME FROM THE FAR SIDE
HOUND OF THE FAR SIDE
THE FAR SIDE OBSERVER
NIGHT OF THE CRASH-TEST DUMMIES
WILDLIFE PRESERVES
WIENER DOG ART
UNNATURAL SELECTIONS
COWS OF OUR PLANET

Anthologies

THE FAR SIDE GALLERY
THE FAR SIDE GALLERY 2
THE FAR SIDE GALLERY 3

THE PREHISTORY OF THE FAR SIDE:
A 10th ANNIVERSARY EXHIBIT

the Far Side

by Gary Larson

WARNER BOOKS

A *Warner* Book

First published in America in 1982 by Andrews and McMeel Inc.,
A Universal Press Syndicate Company, Kansas

First published in Great Britain in 1984
by Futura Publications
Reprinted 1988, 1989, 1990 (twice), 1991
This edition published in 1992 by Warner Books
Reprinted 1993 (twice)

A CIP catalogue record for this book is available from the British Library.

ISBN 0 7515 0235 9

Printed and bound in Great Britain by
BPCC Hazell Books Ltd
Member of BPCC Ltd

Warner Books
A Division of
Little, Brown and Company (UK) Limited
165 Great Dover Street
London SE1 4YA

the Far Side

"Hold still, Carl! . . . Don't . . . move . . . an . . . inch!"

"Egad! . . . Sounds like the farmer's wife has really flipped out this time!"

"Now stay calm . . . Let's hear what they said to Bill."

Today is the first day of the rest of your life.

"Well that's how it happened, Sylvia . . . I kissed this frog, he turns into a prince, we get married and wham! . . . I'm stuck at home with a bunch of pollywogs."

"So! . . . Out bob bob bobbing along again!"

"It's still hungry . . . and I've been stuffing worms into it all day."

"Thank God, Sylvia! We're alive!"

"So! . . . The little sweethearts were going to carve their initials on me, eh?"

"And I've only one thing to say about all these complaints I've been hearing about . . . venison!"

"Say, honey . . . didn't I meet you last night at the feeding-frenzy?"

"Okay, buddy. Then how 'bout the right arm?"

"Through the hoop, Bob! Through the hoop!"

"Something big's going down, sir . . . they're heading your way now!"

"Look at that! . . . Give me the good old days when a man carried a club and had a brain the size of a walnut."

"I've done it! The first real evidence of a
UFO! . . . And with my own camera, in my own
darkroom, and in my own . . ."

"Big Bob says he's getting tired of you saying he doesn't really exist."

"Yeah, Sylvia . . . my set too . . . and in the middle of 'Laverne and Shirley.' "

"Andrew, go out and get your grandfather . . . the squirrels have got him again."

"Thank God! . . . Those blasted crickets have finally stopped!"

"Okay . . . On the count of three everybody rattles."

"So then Carl says to me, 'Look . . . Let's invite over the new neighbors and check 'em out.'"

"One of the nicest evenings I've ever spent at the Wilson's . . . and then you had to go and do that on the rug!"

"The herring's nothin' . . . I'm going for the whole shmeer!"

"We've made it, Warren! . . . The moon!"

"I like it . . . I like it."

"Yoo-hoo! Oh, yoo-hoo! . . . I think I'm getting a blister."

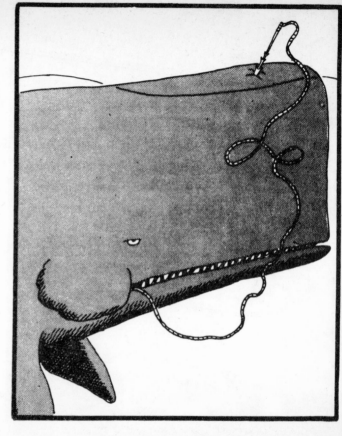

"You imbecile! . . . We flew 12,000 miles for THIS?"

"Oh, brother! . . . Not hamsters again!"

"Well, we're back!"

"Andrew! So that's where you've been! And good heavens! . . . There's my old hairbrush, too!"

"This is a test. For the next thirty seconds, this station will conduct a test of the emergency broadcast system . . ."

"Dear Henry: Where were you? We waited and waited but finally decided that . . ."

"So! . . . You STILL won't talk, eh?"

"Hello, I'm Clarence Jones from Bill's office and . . . Oh! Hey! Mistletoe!"

"This is just not effective . . . We need to get some chains."

"Ho! Just like every time, you'll get about 100 yards out before you start heading back."

"Wouldn't you know it! . . . There goes our market for those things!"

"You meathead! Now watch! . . . The rabbit goes through the hole, around the tree five or six times . . ."

"Excuse me, Harold, while I go slip into something more comfortable."

"We've got the murder weapon and the motive . . . now if we can just establish time-of-death."

"Rejected again, huh Murray? . . . Have you heard about this new breath-freshening toothpaste?"

"Well I'll bet Eggbeater must have missed that one."

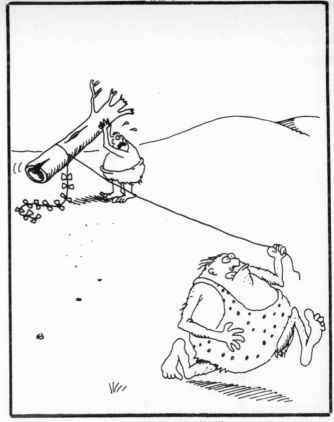

"Okay, Bob! Go! Go!"

"You idiots! . . . We'll never get that thing down the hole!"

"Look . . . You wanna try putting him back together again?"

"Gad, I hate walking through this place at night."

"... and then the second group comes in — 'row, row, row your boat' ..."

"Aphids! Aphids, Henry! . . . Aphids are loose in the garden!"

"Big one, Thag! . . . We caught biiiiig one!"

"Listen . . . this party's a drag. But later on, Floyd, Warren, and myself are going over to Farmer Brown's and slaughter some chickens."

"You're kidding! . . . I was struck twice by lightning too!"

"All units prepare to move in! . . . He's givin' him the
duck now!"

"Still won't talk, huh? . . . Okay, no more Mr. Nice
Guy."

"On the other hand, gentlemen, what if we gave a war and EVERYBODY came?"

"I could have guessed . . . my friends all warned
me that this breed will sometimes turn on you."

"Go get 'em brother."

"See, Frank? Keep the light in their eyes and you can bag them without any trouble at all."

"An excellent specimen . . . symbol of beauty, innocence, and fragile life . . . hand me the jar of ether."

"Wait! Wait! . . . Cancel that, I guess it says 'helf.'"

"I'm afraid you've got cows, Mr. Farnsworth."

"Look. I just don't feel the relationship is working out."

"We're almost free, everyone! . . . I just felt the first drop of rain."

"Okay, Williams, we'll vote . . . how many here say the heart has four chambers?"

"I can't stand it . . . They're so CUTE when they sit like that."

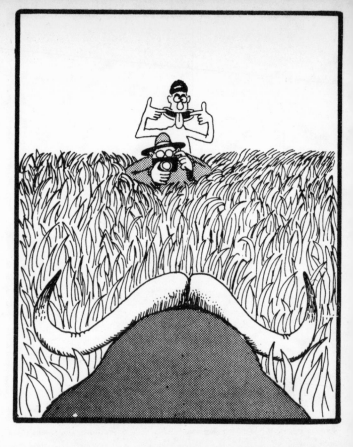

"Don't encourage him, Sylvia."

"Anyone for a chorus of 'Happy Trails'?"

"I asked you a question, buddy . . . What's the square root of 5,248?"

"Early stages of math anxiety"

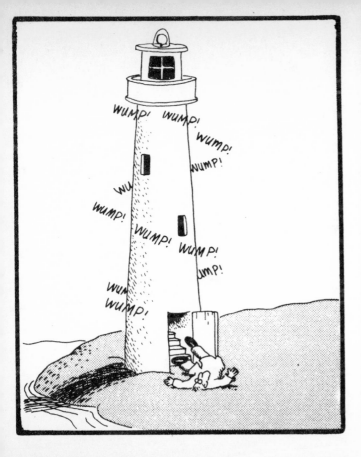
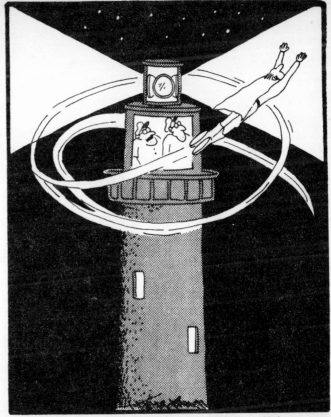

"For God's sake, kill the lights, Murray . . . He's back again!"

"Oh yeah? . . . And I suppose you got those suction marks at the meeting, too!"

"Hey! Look what Zog do!"

"Eraser fight!!"

"And next, for show-and-tell, Bobby Henderson says he has something he found on the beach last summer . . ."

"My word, Walter! . . . Sounded like a good-size bird just hit the window."

"So there he was — this big gorilla just laying there. And Jim says, 'Do you suppose it's dead or just asleep?'"

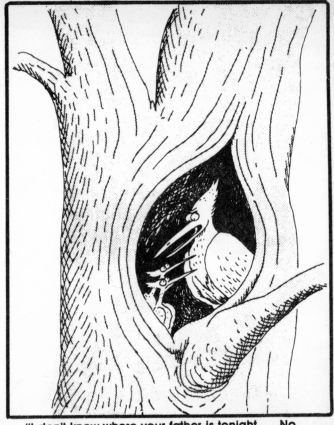

"I don't know where your father is tonight . . . No doubt out bangin' his head against some tree."

"Can I look now?"

"And so I've reached the conclusion, gentlemen, that the Wonker Wiener Company is riddled with incompetence."

"Vive la difference."

"We better do as he says, Thag . . . He's got the drop on us."

"I don't know . . . how many college students do you think you could eat at one time?"

"Well, I never thought about it before . . . but I suppose I'd let the kid go for about $1.99 a pound."

Near Gettysburg, 1863: A reflective moment.

"You heard me, Simmons! . . . You get that cursed bugle fixed!"

"The revolution has been postponed . . . We've discovered a leak."

"I told you guys to slow down and take it easy or something like this would happen."

"Well, so much for the unicorns . . . But, from now on, all carnivores will be confined to 'C' deck."

"Wouldn't you know it! Now the Hendersons have the bomb."

"Sure — but can you make him drink?"

"Knock, knock, knock . . . Ding dong, ding dong . . .
Anybody home? . . . Knock, knock, knock . . ."

"Just nibble at first . . . But when you hear them yell
'Piranha!' — go for it."

"My goodness, Harold . . . Now there goes one big mosquito."

"And remember! . . . I don't want to catch you
bothering the fish!"

"With a little luck, they may revere us as gods."

"Sol You admit that this is, indeed, your banjo the police found at the scene . . . But, you expect this jury to believe you were never in the kitchen with Dinah?"

"Are they gaining, Huxley?"

"Well, when it's my turn, I just hope I go quietly . . .
Without a lot of running around."

"You'll never get away with this!"

"It's no use . . . We've just got to get ourselves a real damsel."

"What? . . . You mean NO ONE brought the buns?"

"Gad! . . . Not *these* Indians again!"

"Hot oil! We need hot oil! . . . Forget the water balloons!"

"Hey, Durk! . . . New roommate, Durk! . . . New roommate! . . . Friend, Durk! . . . Friend! . . ."

"Skinny legs! . . . I got skinny legs!"

"Oh, wow! I can't believe this thing! . . . Does my
voice really sound that funny?"

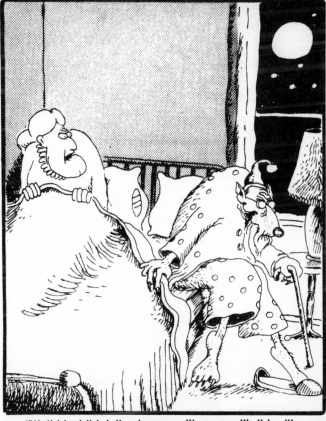

"Well I just think I've been putting up with this silly curse of yours long enough!"

"What a lovely home, Edna! . . . And look at the
fresh newspaper, Stanley!"

"Why, yes . . . we do have two children who won't
eat their vegetables."

"I got a bad feeling about this, Harriet."

"Something's wrong, here, Harriet . . . This is
starting to look less and less like Interstate 95."

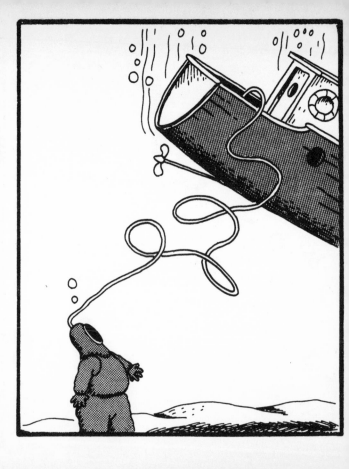

"Quick, Agnes! Look! . . . There it is again!"

"I've got it, too, Omar . . . a strange feeling like we've just been going in circles."

"Hey! I got one! I got one!"

"That settles it, Carl! . . . From now on, you're getting only decaffeinated coffee!"

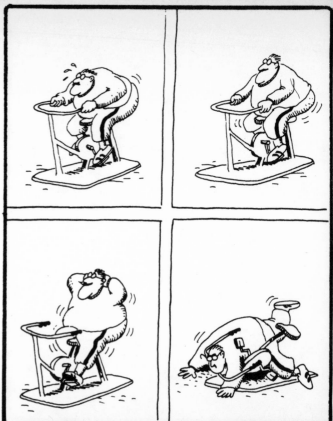

"Oh, Mrs. Oswald . . . you've forgotten something again."

"So then this little sailor dude whips out a can of spinach, this crazy music starts playin', and . . . well, just look at this place."

"And another thing . . . I want you to be more assertive! I'm tired of everyone calling you Alexander the Pretty-Good!"

"Honey, the Merrimonts are here . . . They'd like to come down and see your ape-man project."

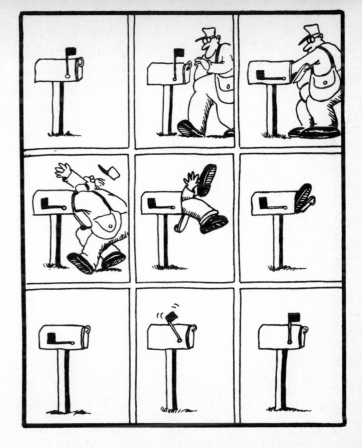

"It seems that agent 6373 has accomplished her mission."

"And now we're going to play she-loves-me, she-loves-me-not!"

"Agnes! It's that heavy, chewing sound again!"

"Don't be alarmed folks . . . He's completely
harmless unless something startles him."

"C'mon! Look at these fangs! . . . Look at these claws! . . . You think we're supposed to eat just honey and berries?"

"Go for it, Sidney! You've got it! You've got it! Good hands! Don't choke!"

"Counterclockwise, Red Eagle! Always counterclock-wise!"

"For twelve perfect years I was a car-chaser. Pontiacs, Fords, Chryslers . . . I took them all on . . . and yesterday my stupid owner backs over me in the driveway."

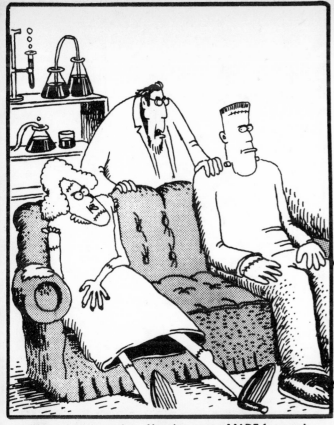

"Hey, c'mon now! . . . You two were MADE for each other!"

"You're embarrassing me, Warren."

"And, as you shall soon observe, we are quite proud of our test tube baby progress."

"Of course, living in an all-glass house has its disadvantages . . . but you should see the birds smack it."

"So! . . . You've been buzzing around the living room again!"

"And so, without further ado, here's the author of 'Mind over Matter' . . ."

"NOW we'll see if that dog can get in here!"

"Okay, Billy . . . Tide's coming in now . . . Dig me out, Billy . . . Billy, I don't want to get angry . . ."

"Remember, milk, eggs, loaf of bread . . . and pick up one of those No-Penguin-Strips."

"C'mon, Sylvia . . . where's your spirit of adventure?"

"I never got his name . . . but he sure cleaned up this town."

"This ain't gonna look good on our report, Leroy."

"For crying out loud! . . . You're ALWAYS hearing
something moving around downstairs!"

"Disgusting! . . . It's just a sort of heavy huffing and puffing."

"Fair is fair, Larry . . . We're out of food, we drew straws — you lost."

"Okay, okay, okay . . . Everyone just calm down and we'll try this thing one more time."

☐	COWS OF OUR PLANET	GARY LARSON	£5.99
☐	WIENER DOG ART	GARY LARSON	£5.99
☐	UNNATURAL SELECTIONS	GARY LARSON	£5.99
☐	BEYOND THE FAR SIDE	GARY LARSON	£4.99
☐	IN SEARCH OF THE FAR SIDE	GARY LARSON	£4.99
☐	BRIDE OF THE FAR SIDE	GARY LARSON	£4.99
☐	VALLEY OF THE FAR SIDE	GARY LARSON	£4.99
☐	HOUND OF THE FAR SIDE	GARY LARSON	£4.99
☐	IT CAME FROM THE FAR SIDE	GARY LARSON	£4.99
☐	THE FAR SIDE OBSERVER	GARY LARSON	£4.99
☐	NIGHT OF THE CRASH-TEST DUMMIES	GARY LARSON	£4.99
☐	WILDLIFE PRESERVES	GARY LARSON	£4.99
☐	THE FAR SIDE GALLERY	GARY LARSON	£6.99
☐	THE FAR SIDE GALLERY 2	GARY LARSON	£6.99
☐	THE FAR SIDE GALLERY 3	GARY LARSON	£6.99
☐	THE PREHISTORY OF THE FAR SIDE	GARY LARSON	£9.99

Warner Books now offers an exciting range of quality titles by both established and new authors which can be ordered from the following address:
Little, Brown and Company (UK) Limited,
P.O. Box 11,
Falmouth,
Cornwall TR10 9EN.
Alternatively you may fax your order to the above address.
Fax No. 0326 376423.

Payments can be made as follows: cheque, postal order (payable to Little, Brown and Company) or by credit cards, Visa/Access. Do not send cash or currency. UK customers and B.F.P.O. please allow £1.00 for postage and packing for the first book, plus 50p for the second book, plus 30p for each additional book up to a maximum charge of £3.00 (7 books plus).

Overseas customers including Ireland, please allow £2.00 for the first book, plus £1.00 for the second book, plus 50p for each additional book.

NAME (Block Letters) ....

ADDRESS ....

....

....

☐ I enclose my remittance for _____

☐ I wish to pay by Access/Visa Card

Number ☐☐☐☐☐☐☐☐☐☐☐☐☐☐☐☐

Card Expiry Date ☐☐☐☐